Animal Tales

by Anne Miranda
illustrated by Craig Spearing

Table of Contents

Jay and Coyote

Once there was a bird called the jay. He was very plain. He was the color of the sand and the bark of trees.

The jay lived near a beautiful lake. He loved the cool blue color of the water. It made him happy to fly over it. One day, the jay went for a swim. He sang a song to the lake as he swam.

"Oh lake, you are beautiful and blue.
I wish that my feathers were as
pretty as you.
If my feathers were blue and not brown.
I'd be the happiest bird around"

The lake liked the song very much. So she changed the color of the jay to blue. The blue jay was very happy.

That day, a coyote went to the lake. The coyote saw the blue jay dancing happily. The coyote was very hungry. But she forgot about her empty stomach. She was jealous of the blue jay's beautiful color. The coyote wanted to be blue, too!

The coyote called, "Brother Jay!"

The blue jay jumped. The coyote had scared him. The blue jay had not seen the coyote creeping along the shore. That is because the coyote was the same color as the sand. The coyote could have eaten the blue jay! The bird flew into a tree. He was safe. "What do you want?" the blue jay asked.

"I want to know why you are beautiful and blue. Tell me your secret, Brother Jay!" the coyote said.

---

creeping: moving slowly

The blue jay did
not want to interfere.
He did not want to help
the coyote. "I live in
the sky," he thought. "If I am
blue, it does not hurt anyone. But
the coyote lives on the earth. If she
is blue, other animals will see her easily.
The coyote will not be able to find food.
Is this a trick?" the blue jay thought.

"Please," cried the coyote. "I want to
be blue!"

"I believe you, Sister Coyote," said the
blue jay. "I will tell you what to do. Go
into the water and sing a song to the
lake. If the lake likes your song, she will
turn you blue."

The blue jay flew away. He was the
same color as the sky.

The coyote jumped into the lake. She began to sing.

"Oh lake, you are a beautiful color blue.
I want to be that color too.
If I could be blue from my head
to my feet,
My life would be very, very sweet."

The lake loved the coyote's song. So she turned the coyote the color blue. The blue coyote was as happy as she could be.

The blue jay saw the coyote. "Sister Coyote, you are beautiful!"

Yes, the coyote was beautiful. She was also still hungry. She decided to eat the blue jay. The coyote chased the blue jay. But the blue jay could see her coming.

"After all I've done for you, you still want to eat me? You will not eat me today or any other day," the blue jay proclaimed.

The coyote was agile. She could run around in circles and jump high in the air. The coyote tried to catch the bird. But she could not catch the blue jay. The blue jay could see the blue coyote easily. But the coyote could not see the blue jay. He was the same color as the sky.

"Sister Coyote, you will never catch me," the blue jay said. "Your blue coat tells me where you are. You will starve." The blue jay flew away.

The coyote tried and tried to catch some food. But Brother Jay was right! The blue coyote could not sneak up on other animals. They always saw her. She felt awkward, or uncomfortable. It was true! She was going to starve.

The beautiful blue coyote fell on the ground. She cried and cried.

"I am a big fool! What did I do? Coyotes are brown. They are not blue!"

Earth heard the coyote. She changed the coyote back to her <u>original</u> color. The happy coyote thanked Earth. Then she went off to find food. The coyote never wanted to change again.

Now the coyote and the blue jay always look for each other. The coyote tries to see the blue jay against the blue sky. And the blue jay watches for the brown coyote creeping along the shore.

<u>original</u>: first

Monkey and Tiger

The monkey was having a very good day. Then she saw a tiger running through the jungle. The monkey knew the tiger would eat her. She had to <u>think fast</u>.

The monkey put banana leaves on a big pile of coconuts. She marched in front of it.

The tiger was curious about the monkey's odd behavior. "What are you doing?" the tiger asked.

"I'm the king's guardian," proclaimed the monkey. "I am guarding the king's food."

<u>think fast</u>: to decide what to do quickly

The tiger had an idea. "The king's royal food will be better than that skinny monkey. I will trick the monkey and get the king's food," he thought.

"You are too small to be the guardian of the king," the tiger said. "I am big. I should be the <u>protector</u> of the king's food."

"Tiger, I am sure the king would like you to guard his food," the monkey said.

"Go now," the tiger said. "I will take good care of the king's food." Then the monkey jumped into the trees and ran away.

"Now the king's food is mine," the tiger declared. He pulled off the banana leaves. Then he bit down hard. The tiger almost broke his teeth.

"Coconuts! That monkey tricked me," the tiger roared. He was very angry.

 **Clue**: <u>Protector</u> means someone who protects, or keeps something safe. Can you find a synonym for <u>protector</u> on this page?

The monkey stopped to rest. Suddenly, she saw the tiger <u>stalking</u> her through the jungle. She had to think fast.

The monkey saw a snake on the ground. The monkey covered the snake with banana leaves. Then she marched in front of it.

Again, the tiger was curious about the monkey's odd behavior. He forgot his anger. "What are you doing?" the tiger asked.

"I am the guardian of the king," proclaimed the monkey. "I am guarding his robes while he swims."

The tiger had another idea. "I will take the king's robes. Then I will be the finest animal in the jungle," the tiger thought. "I will fool the monkey into giving them to me."

<u>stalking</u>: hunting or following

"You are too small to be the guardian of the king," the tiger said. "I am a big animal. I should be the protector of the king's robes."

"Tiger, you are a great animal," the monkey said. "I'm sure the king will let you guard his robes."

"Go now," the tiger said. "I will take good care of the king's robes." The monkey jumped into the trees.

"Now the king's robes will be mine," the tiger said. He ripped off the banana leaves. The snake jumped on the tiger.

"A snake! That monkey tricked me," the tiger roared. "I am very angry," he said.

The monkey saw the tiger racing through the jungle to find her. The monkey had to think fast. She saw a deep hole in the ground. She covered the hole with banana leaves. Then she marched in front of the hole.

Again, the tiger was curious about the monkey's odd behavior. "What are you doing?" the tiger asked.

"I am the guardian of the king," proclaimed the monkey. "I am guarding his <u>treasure</u>."

"I am big," the tiger said. "I should be the guardian of the king's treasure."

"Tiger, I'm sure the king will let you guard his treasure," said the monkey.

<u>treasure</u>: valuable thing, such as gold and jewels

The monkey hid behind a tree. The tiger thought the monkey went away.

"Now the king's treasure will be mine," the tiger said. He pushed off the banana leaves and looked into the deep hole. The tiger could not see the treasure. He bent down a little farther. Then the monkey pushed him in.

The tiger was trapped! "You tricked me," the tiger roared.

"I am small," the monkey said. "But I am very clever. You are big, strong, and handsome. But you are also greedy!" Then the monkey jumped into the trees to escape. She had a very good day.

Language DETECTIVE

Clue: Quotation marks ("_ _") show dialogue, or when people are talking. Can you find more dialogue on this page?

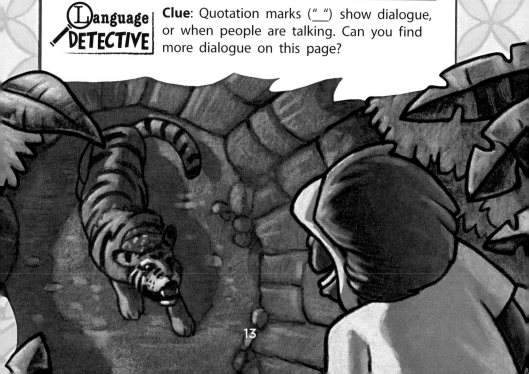

Spider and Turtle

One morning, the spider found some yams. She cooked them on the fire. The hot yams smelled very good. They were soft and sweet. The spider put the yams in a bowl. She hurried to her house. The spider could not wait to eat them all.

Just when the spider sat down, the turtle came to visit. "What is that delicious smell?" the turtle asked.

"Yams," said the spider. "I am about to eat lunch."

"May I join you?" asked the turtle.

The spider did not want to be rude. She asked the turtle to share a meal. But the spider wanted to eat all the yams herself.

---

yams: vegetables similar to sweet potatoes

The spider and turtle sat down at the table. The spider had an idea. The spider said, "You must wash your hands before you eat."

The turtle tottered when he stood up. He almost fell over as he tried to see his hands and feet. "My, my," he said. "My hands are dirty! I will go to the lake to wash them. Will you excuse me?"

"Yes," said the spider.

The turtle went to the lake. The spider could not wait another second. She ate some of the yams.

The turtle washed his hands and feet. Then the turtle went back across the mud to the spider's house. He sat down at the table.

"Forgive me, Turtle," said the spider. "You took so long. I thought you were not going to return. So I <u>ate</u> some of the yams while they were still hot."

"There are many yams left," the turtle said kindly. "And I am still hungry."

"You are still dirty!" the spider said. "Just look at your dirty hands."

The turtle tottered when he stood up. He almost fell over as he tried to see his hands. "You're right", he said. "I am dirty! I will go down to the lake to wash them. Will you excuse me?"

"Yes," said the spider.

Clue: The word <u>ate</u> is an action verb. It tells what the spider did. Can you find more action verbs on this page?

16

The turtle went to the lake. The spider could not wait another second. She ate the rest of the delicious yams.

The turtle washed his hands and feet. Then he wrapped them in leaves so they would not get dirty again. Then he went back across the mud to the spider's house. He sat down.

"Forgive me, Turtle," said the spider. "You took so long. I thought you were not going to return. So I ate the rest of the yams while they were still hot."

"There is nothing left?" the turtle asked. "I am so hungry. I will go home and make some food. Please visit me. I will be happy to share my meal with you."

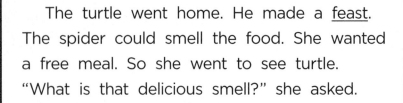

The turtle went home. He made a <u>feast</u>. The spider could smell the food. She wanted a free meal. So she went to see turtle. "What is that delicious smell?" she asked.

"Dinner," the turtle said.

"May I join you?" the spider asked.

The turtle did not want to be rude. So he asked the spider to share a meal.

The turtle's home was on the bottom of the lake. The turtle went in and the spider followed him. But the spider did not sink. She floated at the top of the lake.

<u>feast</u>: very large meal

The spider did not want to miss the feast. She had to think of a way to sink! So she filled the pockets of her vest with stones. Down, down, down the spider went.

The spider was ready to sit down. The turtle said, "It is rude to wear your vest at the table. I have taken my vest off."

The spider did not want to miss a single bite of the turtle's feast. So she took off her vest. Up, up, up she went. The spider tried to dive down. But she was too light. She floated up again and again. The turtle ate every bite of his delicious feast.

Comprehension Check

Summarize the Story

Complete the Author's Purpose chart with the class. Summarize the story. You can use the chart to help you organize your ideas.

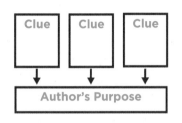

Think and Compare

1. On page 19, the turtle says that it is rude to wear a vest at the table. Why does the turtle say this? *(Evaluate Author's Purpose)*

2. In "Monkey and Tiger," the monkey proclaimed she was the king's guardian. Do you think the monkey's trick was funny or mean? Explain why. *(Synthesize)*

3. In each story, one character learns a lesson. Which lesson did you think was most important? How is this lesson important in real life? *(Apply)*